Disney
MICKEY MOUSE CLUBHOUSE

Quiz It Pen
Ready, Set, Learn!

pi kids® **publications international, ltd.**

Mickey and Daisy buy some fruit.

What color is the piggy bank that Mickey is holding?

★ **red**

★ **purple**

★ **pink**

What letter does *apple* begin with?

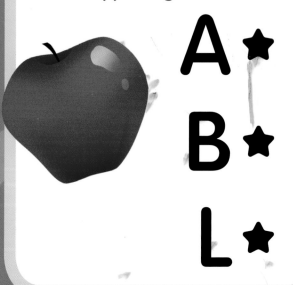

A ★

B ★

L ★

What letter does *pineapple* begin with?

P ★

N ★

E ★

How many apples are in the picture?

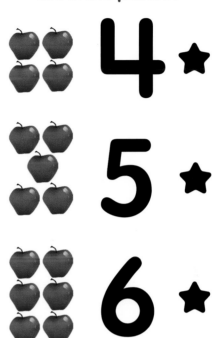

4 ★

5 ★

6 ★

Who is dressed up as a doctor?

Which one is a fruit?

Donald and Daisy like to count animals!

How many frogs are
on the leaves?

 1 ★

 2 ★

 **3** ★

How many birds are
on the branch?

 **4** ★

 **5** ★

 **6** ★

Oh no! Goofy's boat has a hole in it!

Which one rhymes with *boat*?

★

★

★

What color is Goofy's vest?

★ green

★ yellow

★ blue

Mickey likes to read a lot of books.

What shape is the red book?

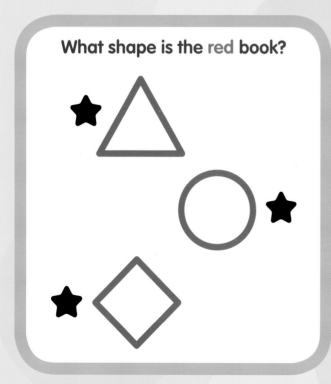

What shape is the yellow book?

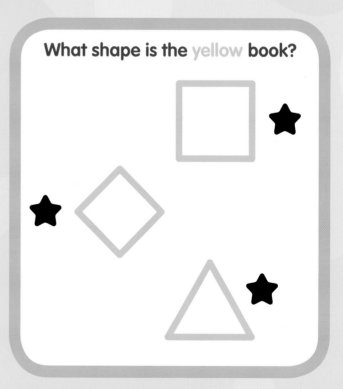

Brrr! It looks like the gang is lost!

Welcome to ANTARCTICA

SANDY BEACH 1111 miles

COOL FOREST 1110 miles

Is it hot or cold in the picture?

★ hot

cold ★

How many penguins are in the picture?

★ 4

★ 5

★ 6

It's clean-up time in the Clubhouse!

Is it daytime or nighttime outside the Clubhouse?

Is Goofy looking up or down?

up

down

What is the weather like outside the Clubhouse?

★

★

★

Which one begins with J?

★

★

★

What letter does *Goofy* begin with?

★ **N**

★ **K**

★ **G**

What color is the plate in Mickey's hand?

★ red

★ blue

★ green

It's hot out in the desert!

Which one tells us which way to go?

What color is the Toon Car?

★ green

★ red

★ yellow

Hot dog! Great job!

It's fun to camp with friends!

Which one is very hot?

Is it daytime or nighttime?

day ★

night ★

Mickey and Minnie see lots of animals.

How many deer does
Mickey see?

5 ★
6 ★
7 ★

How many bunnies does
Minnie see?

8 ★
9 ★
10 ★

What color is Mickey's toothbrush?

★ **red**

★ **black**

★ **green**

Are Pluto and Mickey in the bathroom?

★ **yes**

★ **no**

What do you use to brush your teeth?

Which one of these things would you find in the bathroom?

It's time to get ready for bed!

Do you brush your teeth before or after you go to sleep?

★ **before**

★ **after**

What letter does *Pluto* begin with?

P   L   B

★   ★   ★

What letter does *yummy* begin with?

★ X

★ Y

★ Z

What color is Mickey's hat?

★ green

★ brown

★ white

Is Minnie's plate full or empty?

★ full

★ empty

Are Pluto's eyes open or closed?

★ open

★ closed

It's a hot dog day with friends!

Who is sitting across from Daisy?

Which one rhymes with *phone*?

What number comes after 7?

5 ★

6 ★

8 ★

Solve the addition problem.

• • • •   • • • •

3 + 4 =

★   7

8

9   ★

★

What letter does *rocket* begin with?

R ★

C ★

T ★

What number comes after 9?

★ 7

★ 8

★ 10

Mickey and Pluto count stars in space.

What number is Mickey pointing to?

7 ★

8 ★

9 ★

What letter does *star* begin with?

S ★   T ★   R ★

Donald accidentally knocked over the lemons! What should he say to Pete?

★ **thank you**

★ **please**

★ **I'm sorry**

What rhymes with *clock*?

What shape is the clock?

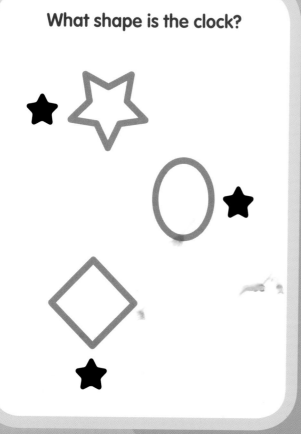

Who is behind the counter?

Oops! Donald made the lemons fall!

What color are the lemons?

★ **green**

★ **red**

★ **yellow**

What letter does *lemon* begin with?

L M N

★   ★   ★

How do you think Donald feels?

What color is the kite?

★ **blue**

★ **green**

★ **red**

Is the kite flying high or low?

★ **high**

★ **low**

Whose name starts with D?

The gang flies up high in the sky!

What shape is the garden?

What letter does *sky* begin with?

B S W

What letter does *window* begin with?

S ★

W ★

P ★

Which one rhymes with *rain*?

How many colors are in this rainbow?

4 ★   5 ★   6 ★

Is Pluto in the picture?

★ yes

★ no

Minnie tells Mickey about rainbows.

What color is Minnie's shoe?

★ orange

★ purple

★ green

What shape is the book?

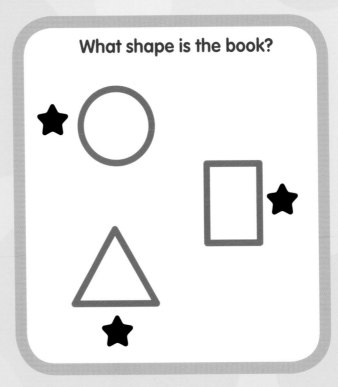

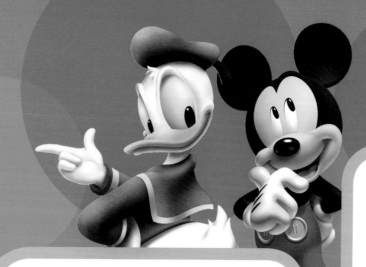

Is the box open or closed?

★ **open**

★ **closed**

Solve the addition problem.

$$2 + 2 =$$

2   **3**   **4**

★   ★   ★

What letter does *hat* begin with?

M   **H**   **T**

★   ★   ★

Which number is greatest?

★ **1**

2 ★

★ **3**

4

★

It's a number roundup!

Solve the subtraction problem.

2 - 1 =

0 1 2

★ ★ ★

What color is Mickey's hat?

★ **brown**

★ **yellow**

★ **pink**

How many yellow flowers are in the vase?

 1 ★

 2 ★

 3 ★

What color is the sky?

★ orange

★ red

★ blue

How do you think Minnie is feeling?

 ★ ☹

 ☺ ★

 ★ 😐

What letter does *Minnie* start with?

★ M

★ N

★ E

Minnie enjoys a picnic with friends.

Who is nearest to Minnie?

What letter does *vase* begin with?

F S V

Which one rhymes with *pail*?

How many sea stars are on the beach?

★ **8**

★ **9**

10

What color is the sign?

★ blue

★ purple

★ yellow

Is there a turtle in the picture?

yes ★

★ no

It's a sunny day at Sandy Beach!

What color are the dolphins?

★ **green**

★ **purple**

★ **gray**

Which one begins with C?

Everyone enjoys playtime.

Which one do you use to make a painting?

Which one plays music?

Mickey likes shapes!

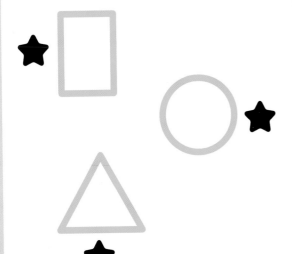

What shape is the yellow door?

What color is the triangle door?

★ **pink**

★ **blue**

★ **yellow**

What letter does *tent* begin with?

T N D
★ ★ ★

What is Minnie pointing at?

Who looks sleepy?

What color is the backpack?

★ red

★ green

★ pink

It's a campout under the stars.

What letter does *owl* end with?

O ★

W ★

L ★

Which one rhymes with *star*?

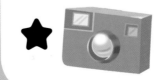

How is Pluto feeling?

How many ducklings are in the picture?

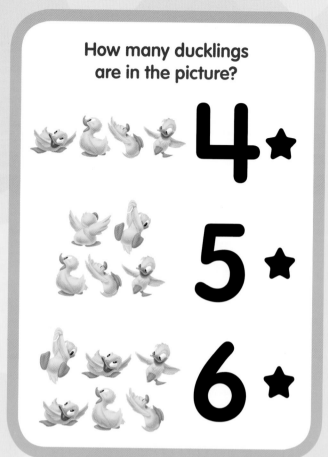

4 ★

5 ★

6 ★

What letter does *duck* begin with?

T D K

Is there a butterfly in the picture?

★ yes

★ no

The ducklings want to play with Pluto!

What color is Pluto's bow?

★ green

★ purple

★ pink

Which one rhymes with *bee*?

Is Minnie in front of or behind the Toon Car?

★ **in front**

★ **behind**

What shape is on Donald's ball?

What letter does *umbrella* begin with?

B ★

U ★

A ★

What colors are on Daisy's umbrella?

★ **yellow**

★ **red**

★ **green**

★ **blue**

The gang gets ready for a fun day!

Which one rhymes with *night*?

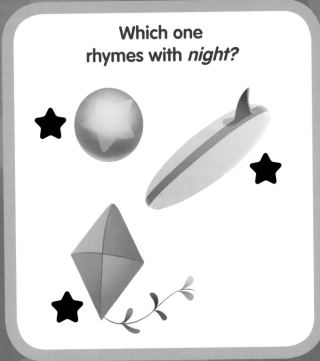

What color is Donald's ball?

★ orange

★ purple

★ green

What letter does *basket* begin with?

T B S
★ ★ ★

Which of these fruits is Daisy using in her salad?

★
★
★

What color is Daisy's shirt?

★ **purple**

★ **pink**

★ **orange**

Which one rhymes with *moon*?

★
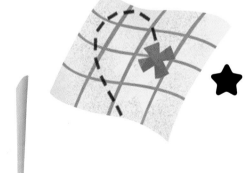
★

★

Daisy makes a fruit salad for a picnic.

Is the faucet on or off?

★ on

★ off

Which one ends with the letter N?

★

★

★

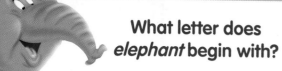

What letter does _elephant_ begin with?

T E L

★ ★ ★

Which animal is tallest?

Is Pluto in front of or behind Minnie?

★ in front

★ behind

What shape is the sun?

It's a parade!

Which of these animals has fur?

★

★

★

Is there a rabbit in the picture?

★ **yes**

★ **no**

How many lizards are in the picture?

1 ★

2 ★

3 ★

How do you think Pluto feels?

★

 ★

★

What letter does *rabbit* begin with?

★ P

★ N

★ R

Which one rhymes with *rake?*

 ★

 ★

★